1001 Things to Find

Princesses

igloobooks

Can you find 1001 princess things?

Welcome to Princess Sophia and Princess Daisy's beautiful kingdom. The Queen has invited everyone to a special banquet. She tells the guests about a very wealthy king from many years before, who hid his finest fortune somewhere in the royal kingdom. As time passed, the treasure was forgotten, until one day, a clue was discovered.

"Find 12 golden keys to discover the finest treasure in the land," it read.

Join Princess Sophia and Princess Daisy as they search for the golden keys. In each scene, you will need to find Princess Sophia, Princess Daisy and a golden key. There are over 1000 pretty items for you to find along the way, too, so let's get treasure hunting!

Princess Sophia   Golden key   Princess Daisy

On the opposite page, see if you can spot Princess Sophia, Princess Daisy and the golden key. Once you've found them, see if you can spot the items below, too.

2 violinists

9 red cherries

11 pretty cupcakes

Sleepover Secret

At the royal sleepover, Princess Sophia and Princess Daisy tell their friends about the treasure mystery. Can you spot Sophia and Daisy among the other princesses? Remember to find a golden key, too.

1 pretty
rocking horse

4 polka-dot
sleeping bags

5 pretty
carousels

6 blue
toothbrushes

7 stripy
pillows

8 hot-water
bottles

9 dotty,
purple slippers

10 cups of
hot chocolate

11 green
eye masks

13 bottles
of nail polish

The King's Kitchen

In the morning, the princesses help the royal chef to bake lots of tasty treats for their busy day of treasure hunting ahead. Can you find Princess Sophia, Princess Daisy and a golden key?

5 rainbow cupcakes

6 polka-dot oven gloves

8 castle-shaped jellies

12 jars of strawberry spread

15 sparkly chef hats

Royal Wardrobe

In the dressing room, there are so many elegant dresses and sparkly shoes that the princesses have forgotten what they were looking for. Can you spot Princess Sophia, Princess Daisy and the next key?

5 velvet cushioned stools

6 purple pompom shoes

8 heart-shaped bags

12 perfume bottles

15 gold hand mirrors

Princess Pool Party

Splosh! At the exotic swimming pool, the princesses dive into in the sparkling, crystal-clear water. Find Princess Sophia and Princess Daisy. Then, help them by finding the next golden key.

1 royal
lifeguard

4 stripy
parasols

5 gold
mermaid statues

6 pairs of
orange armbands

7 fluffy,
pink towels

8 Hawaiian
garlands

9 dotty
rubber rings

10 stripy
beach balls

11 tropical
juice drinks

13 yellow
flip-flops

Perfect Pirouettes

The princesses explore the dance hall for another golden key.
They spin, whirl, leap and twirl in time to the enchanting music.
Can you find Princess Sophia, Princess Daisy and another key?

5 pretty
dance bags

6 stripy
ballet outfits

8 princesses in
swan costumes

12 twirling
dance ribbons

15 gold
dance prizes

Castle Cafe

What a busy morning! The princesses enjoy lunch at the Castle Cafe before continuing their treasure hunt. Spot Princess Sophia and Princess Daisy. Then, help them to find a golden key.

5 juicy, red apples

6 swirly cinnamon buns

8 ice-cream sundaes

12 vases of pretty flowers

15 royal milkshakes

Best in Show

Giddy-up! At the royal stables, the princesses groom their prize-winning ponies and search for another golden key. Can you spot Princess Sophia and Princess Daisy?

1 princess feeding a horse

4 silver trophies

5 black riding hats

6 horses wearing tiaras

7 brown saddles

8 grooming brushes

9 stable brooms

10 shiny horseshoes

11 crunchy carrots

13 pink rosettes

Picnics in the Park

After a busy afternoon of searching for hidden keys, the princesses are enjoying a well-deserved picnic. Can you find Princess Sophia and Princess Daisy? Help them by finding a golden key, too.

5 princess swings

6 stripy rainbow kites

8 cute ducklings

12 busy bumblebees

15 picnic baskets

Tree-house Den

Later, the princesses gather in their tree-house den to discuss the treasure hunt. Where could the next key be hiding? Find Princess Sophia and Princess Daisy, then, help them to find a golden key.

5 pretty
paint palettes

6 sparkly
violins

8 secret
rincess journals

12 balls
of wool

15 bowls of
ainbow sweets

The Fairest Kingdom

News of the treasure hunt has travelled far and wide and more princesses have arrived in their carriages to join in. Spot Princess Sophia and Princess Daisy. Then, find another golden key.

1 princess
watering flowers

4 fairy
fountains

5 candy-shaped
trees

6 green
wheelbarrows

7 green
gardening gloves

8 golden
watering cans

9 friendly
caterpillars

10 pretty,
pink roses

11 garden
gnomes

13 pretty,
little bugs

Attic Antics

In a dark attic of the tallest tower in the palace, the princesses search through chests and boxes. Find Princess Sophia and Princess Daisy in the shadows and help to find a golden key.

5 silver knights

6 chests of fancy dress

8 ornate candelabra

12 antique teddy bears

15 cute spiders

The Great Library

1 purple
secret door

8 spinning
globes

10 green
feather quills

12 pairs of
pink glasses

15 paper
planes

Mystery Solved

At last, the treasure has been found! From behind the secret door, sparkling jewels and shiny golden coins glitter brightly. Can you spot Princess Sophia and Princess Daisy among the treasure?

1 princess wearing a robe

4 blue treasure chests

5 gold elephant statues

6 crowns on red, velvet cushions

7 cats wearing pearl necklaces

8 cute, little mice

9 ruby and gold goblets

10 emerald heart gems

11 musical trinket boxes

13 sparkly diamond rings

Celebration Time

Princess Sophia and Princess Daisy hold a grand ball to celebrate. It's been a tricky mystery to solve, but it's been so much fun. Can you spot Princess Sophia and Princess Daisy?

1 sparkling
glass slipper

4 puppies in
bow ties

5 large
fruit bowls

6 sparkly
rainbow dresses

7 pink,
swirly lollipops

8 gold
goblets

9 blue
balloons

10 pieces of
raspberry cake

11 fun
party hats

13 pretty
party bags

Well done! You've helped the princesses to solve the great treasure mystery.
Now go back and see if you can find each of these royal characters
and items in every scene, too.

The King

The Queen

Charlie the cat

Royal tortoise

Ruby tiara

Teapot

Diamond

The King's
throne

How closely were you looking at each scene?
Go back and see if you can spot which scene each of these items was hidden in.

A princess painting
on an easel

A princess sat on
a pile of books

Game of
skittles

Three ice-cream
mountains